Scott Foresman

Reading

Favorite Things Old and New

About the Cover Artist
Maryjane Begin and her family live in Providence, Rhode Island, where she teaches college
students when she is not working on her own art. Many of her illustrations—even of imaginary
places—show how things in Providence look.

ISBN 0-673-59639-7

5 6 7 8 9 10-VH-06 05 04 03 02 01 00

Scott Foresman Reading

Favorite Things Old and New

Program Authors

Peter Afflerbach

James Beers

Camille Blachowicz

Candy Dawson Boyd

Deborah Diffily

Dolores Gaunty-Porter

Violet Harris

Donald Leu

Susan McClanahan

Dianne Monson

Bertha Pérez

Sam Sebesta

Karen Kring Wixson

Scott Foresman

Editorial Offices: Glenview, Illinois • New York, New York
Sales Offices: Reading, Massachusetts • Duluth, Georgia • Glenview, Illinois
Carrollton, Texas • Menlo Park, California

Contents

Favorite Things Old and New

4

THREE BY THE SEA

by Edward Marshall
pictures by James Marshall

Morris and Boris
Three Stories

Favorite Things Old and New

How do things get to be favorites?

The Red Stone Game

by Mary Blount Christian
illustrated by Elizabeth Allen

"Oh, no!" Gale said.
"The stone in my ring
is missing!"

Nate and Pam came in.
"Did you call us?" they asked.
"I have to find my stone,"
said Gale.

"We just made cookies
with Mom," said Nate. "Did
you have it before we made
cookies?"

"Yes," said Gale.

"Did you have it after we
made cookies?" Pam asked.
"No," Gale said.

"It must be someplace!
Let's play a game called Find
the Red Stone," said Pam.

14

Nate looked on the floor.
Pam looked in the sink. Gale
looked in the pan.

Something made Gale laugh.

She picked up a cookie.

"I see something," she said.

"The face of this cookie has a red nose!" said Gale. Gale, Nate, and Pam laughed as they all ate cookies. No one ate the cookie with the red nose!

17

The Gingerbread Man

retold by Sally Bell
illustrated by Bob Barner

A woman and a man
lived on a farm.
The woman said,
"I will make a
gingerbread man."
So she did.

19

Soon she heard something.

She looked.

The gingerbread man jumped out.

The woman wanted to catch him.
The man wanted to catch him.
But the gingerbread man ran away.

The gingerbread man ran fast.

He laughed.

He sang,

"Run, run, as fast as you can.

You can not catch me.

I am the gingerbread man!"

He saw a man.

"Stop!" called the man.

"I want something to eat.

You look good."

The gingerbread man ran on.

The man ran after him.

The gingerbread man laughed.
He sang,
"Run, run, as fast as you can.
You can not catch me.
I am the gingerbread man!"

He saw a girl.

26

"Stop!" called the girl.
"I want something to eat.
You look good."
The gingerbread man ran on.
The girl ran after him.

The gingerbread man laughed.
He sang,
"Run, run, as fast as you can.
You can not catch me.
I am the gingerbread man!"

He saw a boy.

"Stop!" called the boy.

"I want something to eat.

You look good."

The gingerbread man ran on.

The boy ran after him.

The gingerbread man laughed.

He sang,

"Run, run, as fast as you can.

You can not catch me.

I am the gingerbread man!"

The gingerbread man saw water.

He stopped.

He did not know what to do.

The gingerbread man saw a fox.

The fox saw him.

The gingerbread man sang,
"Run, run, as fast as you can.
You can not catch me.
I am the gingerbread man!"

The fox said, "I do not want to catch you.
I will help you.
You can ride on me."

The gingerbread man got
on the fox.
The fox jumped into the water.
The fox said,
"You will get wet.
Ride on my head."
The gingerbread man did.

The fox said,
"You will get wet.
Ride on my nose."
The gingerbread man did.
The fox put his head up.
The gingerbread man fell.

Snap!

The fox ate him up.

And that was the end

of the gingerbread man.

About the Illustrator

Bob Barner uses special papers to make his pictures. He cuts and tears the papers just the way he wants them. Then he glues them down. He finishes his work with pencils and pastels. For this story, he made a clay gingerbread man. The clay made it look like a real cookie.

Mr. Barner says, "The fox is my favorite character in this story. I like the way he looks."

Let's Talk

If you were in this story, who would you be? Why?

Write a New Ending

What if the gingerbread man got away from the fox? What would he do next?

1. Write a new ending for the story.

2. Draw a picture for your new ending.

Mix, Bake, and Eat!

A **verb** tells what a person, animal, or thing does.

Many verbs are action words.

The boy **puts** on the sprinkles.
The cat **licks** the milk.

Talk

Look at the picture.
Tell what the people do.
Tell what the animals do.
Tell what the things do.

Write

Write a sentence about something you do.
What action word will you use?

The Same as You

by Sharon Fear

illustrated by
Stacey Schuett

"Grandpa? Was Mother like me when she was little?" asked Katie.

"Yes, she was," said Grandpa. "Your mother was brave. She liked to jump into the water. The same as you."

"Your mother got good grades.
She made all of us proud every
day. The same as you."

"Grandpa? Was Grandmother like me?" asked Katie.

"Yes, she was," said Grandpa.

"Your grandmother was thin. She had thick, black hair. Her name was Katie. The same as you."

"Your grandmother liked to bake.
She made cakes like this. She
made all of us laugh every day.
The same as you."

"Grandpa? Am I like you?" asked Katie.

"Oh, no," said Grandpa. "I am the checkers champ. No one plays checkers like me! I plan to win every game."

"Oh, Grandpa!" said Katie. "I plan to win every game too. One day I *will* be the same as you."

Cherry Pies and Lullabies

by Lynn Reiser

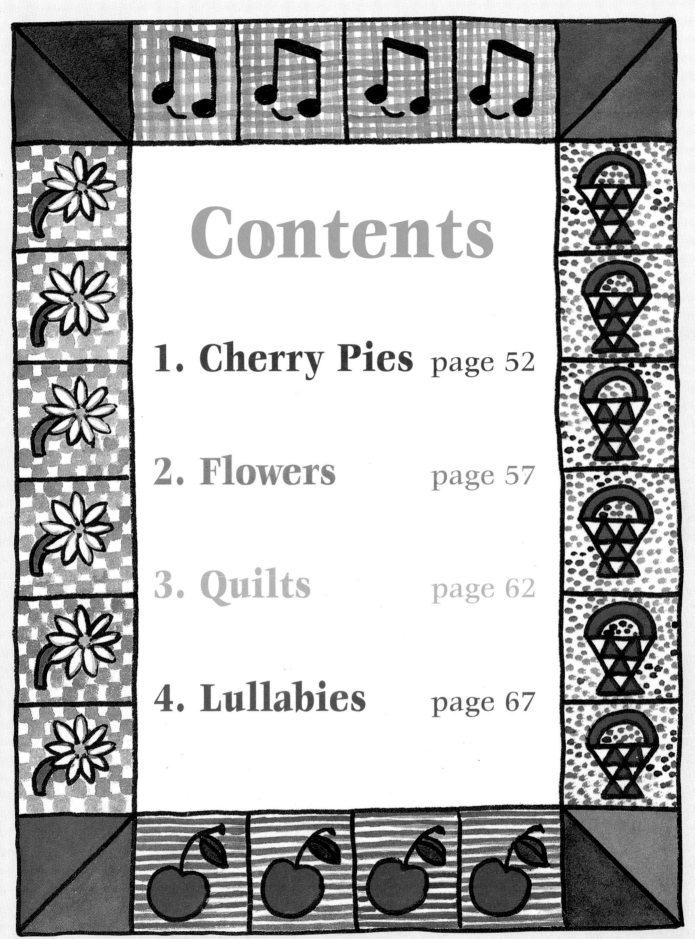

Contents

1. Cherry Pies

My great-grandmother
baked a cherry pie
for my grandmother.

My grandmother
baked a cherry pie
for my mother.

My mother
baked a cherry pie
for me.

And I
baked a cherry pie
for my bear.

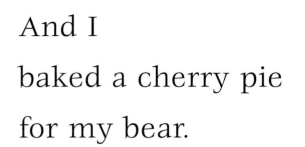

Every time it was the same, but different.

2. Flowers

My great-grandmother
made a crown of flowers
for my grandmother.

My grandmother
made a crown of flowers
for my mother.

My mother made
a crown of flowers
for me.

And I made
a crown of flowers
for my bear.

Every time it was the same, but different.

3. Quilts

My great-grandmother
gave a quilt
to my grandmother.

My grandmother
gave a quilt
to my mother.

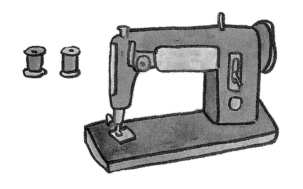

My mother
gave a quilt
to me.

And
I gave a quilt
to my bear.

Every time it was the same, but different.

4. Lullabies

My great-grandmother
sang a lullaby
to my grandmother.

My grandmother
sang a lullaby
to my mother.

My mother
sang a lullaby
to me.

I sang
a lullaby
to my bear.

And every time
it was the same.

 # Lullaby

words by Lynn Reiser   music by Johannes Brahms

Lul - la- by and good-night. Pie is   sweet, stars are

bright.__   Close your eyes__ un- til   day. ___   In your

dreams__laugh and play. Crowned with flow-   ers you

sleep,__wrapped in love soft and   deep.___ Close your

eyes__ now and stay__wrapped in love un- til   day.

About the Author and Illustrator

Lynn Reiser

   Cherry Pies and Lullabies is about Lynn Reiser's family. The people in her family have lived in different places. Her grandmother lived on a farm. Her mother lived in a small town. Ms. Reiser lived in a suburb. Now Ms. Reiser has a niece who lives in a city.

   Lynn Reiser says that life has changed for her family, but some things "like lullabies, are always the same."

Reader Response

Let's Talk

Pretend you are the girl in the story. Why do you make each gift for your bear?

Make a Treasure Box

What you need:

shoe box

paper

art supplies

What you do:

1

Paste paper on your shoe box.

2

Color your box.
Add things to it.

 3

Put things inside that are special to you.

One Can Do It

Verbs may tell what one person, animal, or thing does. Add **-s** to these verbs.

My uncle **plays** the piano. Grandmother **sings**.

Talk

Tell about one grown-up you know.

What does that person do?

What verb will you use?

Write

Write a letter to someone in your family.

Tell what you have been doing.

Rose and Grandma Make the Sun Shine

by Juanita Havill

illustrated by
Darryl Ligasan

"Where can we go for our
family picnic?" Grandma said.
"Lone Lake!" said Rose and
Kevin and their mother and father.

"Everybody has to help," Dad
said. "I'll shop for things to eat."
"I'm going to make cakes,"
said Mom.

"I'll call the rest of the family," said Kevin.

"I'm going to play games with the little kids," said Rose.

She wrote a list of things to do.

"What are you going to do, Grandma?" said Rose.

"I'll think of something," said Grandma.

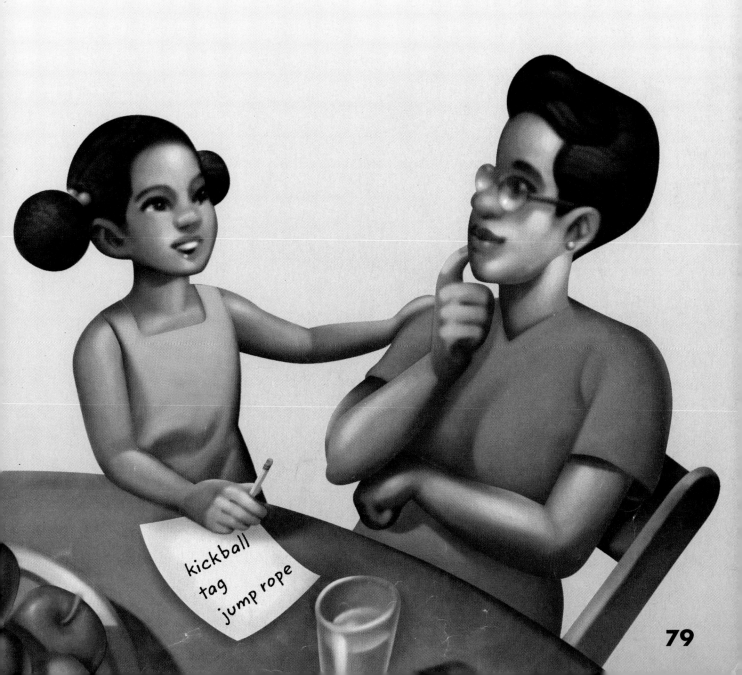

The family went to Lone Lake.

"Look at those clouds," said Kevin.

"We'll have to go home."

"No, we don't. I have a plan,"
Grandma said.

"Who has stories to tell?" said

Grandma.

"I have one," said Rose.

The family sat close by the stove.

They all had a turn. After a
while, the sun shone.

"Thank you, Grandma," said
Rose. "You had a very good plan."

"Our stories made the sun shine," said Grandma.

Our Family Get-Together

by Carmen Tafolla and
Israel Tafolla Bernal

Last fall we had a big family
get-together. My father had the idea.
But it was my idea too.

Everyone came to the same place at the same time. They came to my uncle's ranch in Texas. Then we just had fun together.

Some came by car.

Some came by plane.

Uncle Richard just walked.

The get-together was at

his ranch.

There were so many cousins at the get-together. There were brothers, sisters, fathers, mothers, uncles, aunts, and grandmothers!

All of us came with something. My father came with hot dogs. My uncle came with a watermelon. And what did I come with? My best joke!

Uncle Richard has
horses on his ranch.
He has cows and
sheep too.

Grandma showed us an old
picture. It was Grandpa's
father. He had on a hat and
rode a horse.

I rode a horse too.

My father held the rope.

My mother took a picture of me.

I was going to look like

Grandpa's father!

I met a new cousin.

Ronnie was six like me.

He liked jokes too.

We looked for frogs.

And we saw a lot of them!

The frogs went up a

tree very fast.

They were very little.

My cousin saw three.

I saw five.

We saw more than frogs.

We saw a big fence and

two very old wheels.

Late in the day, my sister
and my cousin put on a
show. It was sunny, so we
sat in the shade.

Mother made a family tree.

A family tree shows all the

names in the family.

Here is my name.

We didn't want the fun to stop.

But it was time to go home.

"Thank you for this get-together,"
said Mother. "I hope we'll see you
again soon."

I didn't know my family was so big.

I met a new cousin. It was fun to
look for frogs with him. Next year,
I will find more frogs!

I bet next year I will find
more cousins too.

Carmen Tafolla wrote this story together with her son, Israel. It tells about their family get-together at a ranch near San Antonio, Texas. Dr. Tafolla and her son wrote this story as if only Israel were speaking.

At the get-together, Israel really did meet a new cousin. And he met some frogs too!

Four Generations

by Mary Ann Hoberman

Sometimes when we go out for walks,
I listen while my father talks.

The thing he talks of most of all
Is how it was when he was small

And he went walking with *his* dad
And conversations that they had

About *his* father and the talks
They had when *they* went out for walks.

Let's Talk

What was the best part of the get-together? Why? What else would you want to do at a family get-together?

Family Get-Together
Saturday
Sept. 2 2:00

Make an Invitation

You are the boy in the story. Make an invitation for your family get-together.

Family Picnic

Verbs may tell what two or more people, animals, or things do. These verbs do <u>not</u> have **-s** added.

The children **eat**.
The men **bring** the food.

Talk

Look at the picture.
Find two or more people, animals, or things.
Tell what they do.

Write

Write about what people in your family do together.

The Rolling Rice Cake

A Story from Japan

retold by Eric A. Kimmel
illustrated by Oki S. Han

An old man was going to cut
wood. His wife made pretty rice
cakes for him.

"Thank you," the old man said.
"You make the best rice cakes!"

The old man cut lots of
wood. Soon he wanted a
rice cake. The rice cake
fell out of his hand. It
rolled down a hole.

The old man looked down. He heard a pretty song.

"Rolling rice cake is so nice. Roll a cake to your friends the mice!"

It was a family of mice.
"Sing again!" the old man
said. He rolled down his rice
cakes. The mice sang as
they ate them.

The old man wanted to
be closer. He wanted to
hear the singing better.
He fell into the hole and
rolled to the bottom.

"Nice old man," the mice said.
"Here is a present. A little bag
of rice."

"Thank you," the old man
said. "Can you help me out of
this hole?"

The mice sang this song.

"Rolling old man is so nice.
We'll help our friend.
He fed the mice."

Soon the mice rolled the
old man out of the hole!

The old man took the rice
bag home. The man and his
wife never ran out of rice.
There was always lots of rice
to make rice cakes for all.

The Rat and the Cat

by Edward
Marshall

illustrated by
James Marshall

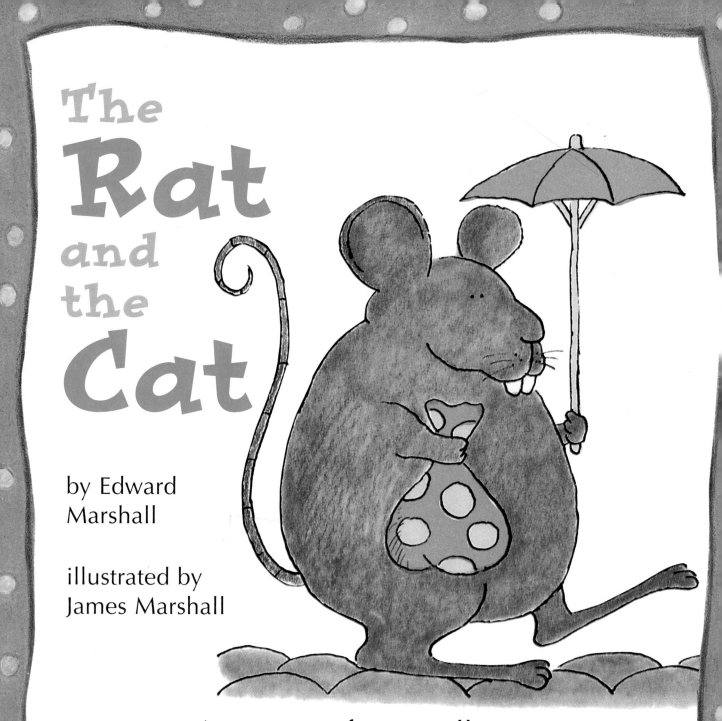

A rat went for a walk.

"What a fine day," he said.

"The sun is shining
and all is well."

Soon he came to a shop.

"My, my," said the rat.

"What a pretty cat.

And I have never had a cat."

"I will buy that cat
and have a friend," he said.
And he went into the shop.
"I want a cat," he said.

"Are you sure you want a *cat?*"
asked the owner.

"I am sure," said the rat.
"And I want that one."

"That will be ten cents,"
said the man.
"If you are *sure.*"

"I am sure," said the rat.
"Here is my last dime.
Give me my cat."

The rat and the cat left the shop.

"We will be friends," said the rat.

"Do you think so?" said the cat.

"Well, we'll see."

The rat and the cat sat
in the sun.
"What do you do for fun?"
asked the rat.

"I like to catch things,"
said the cat.

"That's nice," said the rat.

"I am hungry," said the cat.
"How about lunch?"

"A fine idea," said the rat.
"What is your favorite dish?"

"I do not want to say,"
said the cat.

"You can tell me," said the rat.
"We are friends."

"Are you *sure* you want to
know?" said the cat.

"I am sure," said the rat.
"Tell me what you like to eat."

"I will tell you," said the cat.
"But let us go where
 we can be alone."

"Fine with me," said the rat.

The cat and the rat
went to the beach.
"I know," said the rat. "Fish.
You like to eat fish."

"Not at all," said the cat.
"It's much better than fish."

"Tell me," said the rat.
"I just *have* to know."

"Come closer," said the cat.

"And I will tell you."

"Yes?" said the rat.

"What I like," said the cat, "is . . ."

". . . CHEESE! I love cheese!"

"So do I," said the rat.
"And I have some here."

"Hooray!" said the cat.
"And now we are friends."

So they sat on the beach
and ate the cheese.

And that was that.

About the Author and Illustrator

Edward Marshall and James Marshall were the same person! James Marshall's middle name was Edward. Sometimes he used the name James. Other times he used the name Edward. For "The Rat and the Cat" he used both names!

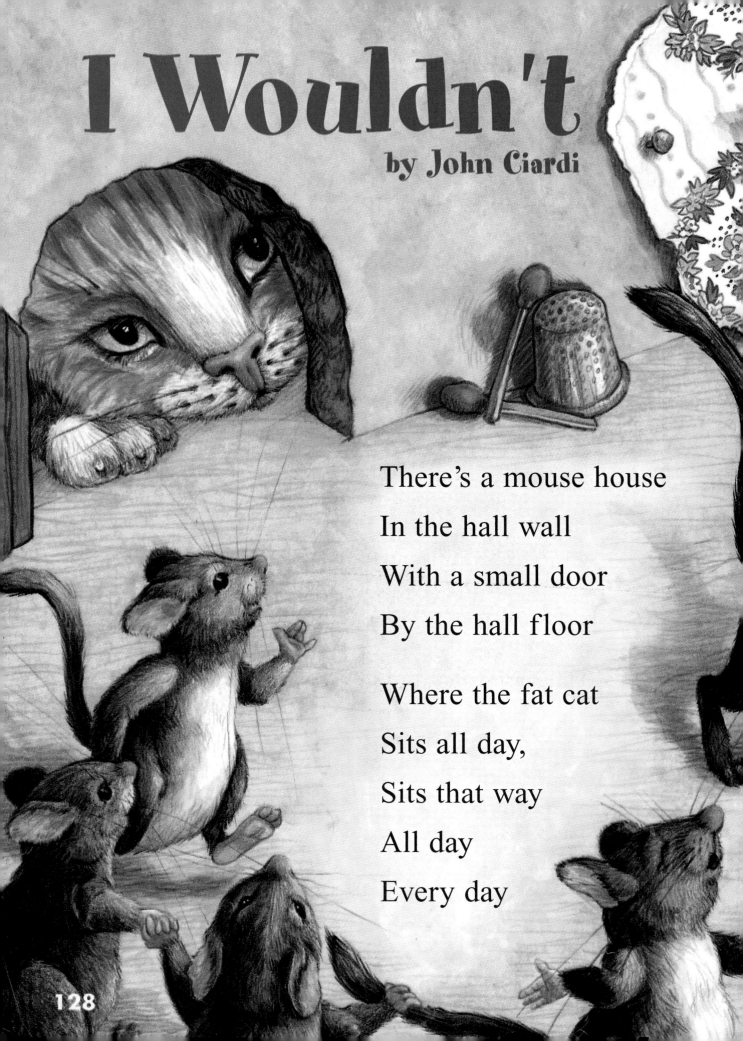

I Wouldn't

by John Ciardi

There's a mouse house
In the hall wall
With a small door
By the hall floor

Where the fat cat
Sits all day,
Sits that way
All day
Every day

Just to say,
"Come out and play"
To the nice mice
In the mouse house
In the hall wall
With the small door
By the hall floor.

And do they
Come out and play
When the fat cat
Asks them to?

Well, would you?

Let's Talk

If you were the rat, would you buy a cat? Why or why not?

Let's Be Friends

Now pretend you are the cat. Why would you want the rat to be your friend?

Tell two reasons to a classmate.

We Cook, We Cooked

Verbs can tell about action that takes place now.

The children **mix** the lemonade.

Verbs can tell about action that happened in the past. Add **-ed** to the verb.

The children **mixed** the lemonade.

Talk

What have you cooked? Tell how you cooked it.

Write

Write about two of your favorite foods.

June and the Mule
A Tall Tale
by Eric A. Kimmel
illustrated by Kenneth Spengler

"The ranch can use some rain,"
said June.
She looked up to watch the sky.
She looked for clouds.

A funny cloud came by.

There were four legs on the cloud.

There were long ears on it.

It looked like a mule.

"I think I can catch it," June said.

She flung her rope.

That rope went a long, long way.

June got the mule.

The funny mule bucked.

He jumped and kicked.

June used her rope to pull

the mule down.

June jumped on the mule.

She rode with him in the sky.

June took out her flute.

"I'll play a tune for the mule!"

she said.

Then June sang,

"Cute mule, funny mule,
Make the sky clang and bang!
Ring! Ding! Make it rain!
Drop by drop! Inch by inch!"

The mule kicked both back legs.
His kicks made thunder crash
and lightning flash.
He made rain fall from the sky.

The rain ended.

The mule wanted to stay with June.

"Stick around," she said.

"I'll call you Jules!"

Slim, Luke, and the Mules

by Stewart Christopher

illustrated by Wendy Shaul

Slim and Luke were cowboys

a long time ago.

They lived on a big ranch.

The ranch was a long way from town.

Slim and Luke had five mules.

One day Slim said,
"We are out of food.
We have to go to town.
We can use the mules to
bring the food home."

Slim and Luke lined up the mules.
Slim got on the mule at the
front of the line.
Luke got on the mule at the
end of the line.

Luke said, "How will we get all five mules to town? We may lose one."

Slim said, "You watch the mules. That way we will not lose one."

The cowboys left for town with the mules.

Soon Slim looked back at Luke. Slim said, "Are all five mules here?"

Luke said, "I think so. I have been watching them the whole time. I will count them."

Luke pointed at the mules in line in
front of him. He counted,
"One mule,
two mules,
three mules,
four mules."

"Four mules!" said Luke.
"That's funny.
I have been watching the mules.
How did we lose one?
I will count them again."

Luke counted the mules in
front of him again.
He counted four mules.
"We *have* lost a mule," he said.

Slim said, "I will count the mules."
Slim pointed at the mules in line in
back of him. He counted,

"One mule,
two mules,
three mules,
four mules."

Then he said,
"Luke, I counted four mules too.
We have lost a mule.
We have to find it."

The cowboys got down and
began to look.
They both looked and looked
for that lost mule.
But they didn't find it.
At last Luke said, "That mule
must be lost for good."

Slim said, "Let's go back and
count the mules again.
Maybe more mules are
lost by now."

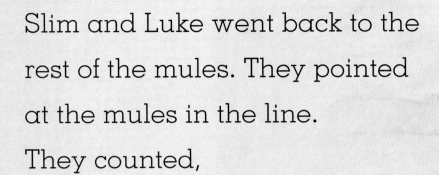

Slim and Luke went back to the
rest of the mules. They pointed
at the mules in the line.
They counted,

"One mule,
two mules,
three mules,
four mules,
five mules."

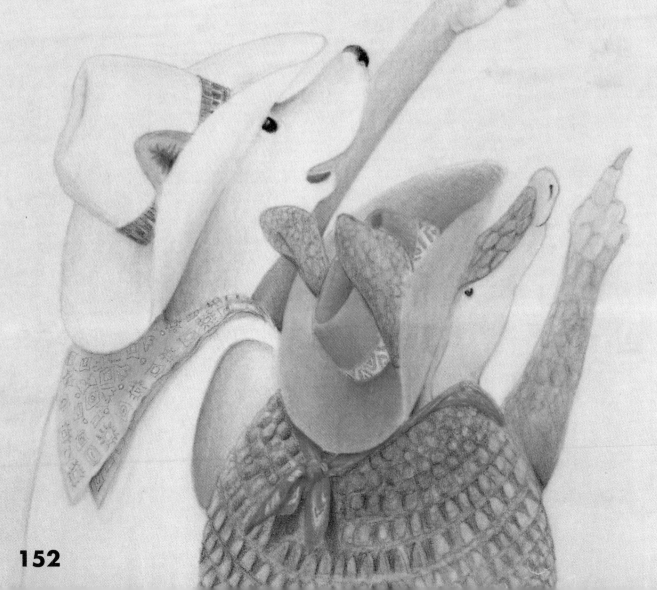

Slim said, "What do you know!
The lost mule is back."

Then Luke said, "Now we can
go to town."

And that's what they did.

Slim and Luke's Animals

These are the animals on Slim and Luke's ranch.

mules   horses   cattle   pigs

This bar graph also shows how many animals Slim and Luke have.

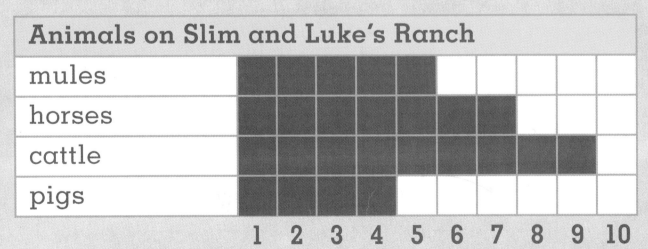

Animals on Slim and Luke's Ranch

	1	2	3	4	5	6	7	8	9	10
mules	■	■	■	■	■					
horses	■	■	■	■	■	■	■			
cattle	■	■	■	■	■	■	■	■	■	
pigs	■	■	■	■						

Let's Talk

Which animals do they have the most of?
Which animals do they have the fewest of?

154

About the Illustrator

Wendy Shaul grew up in the Southwest. She loves snakes, lizards, and other critters. She also loves art, so she put her two interests together. Now she's an artist who often draws animals.

Ms. Shaul saw her first armadillo in Costa Rica. She remembered it when she drew Luke for this story.

Reader Response

Let's Talk

Tell Slim and Luke what was wrong.

Readers Theater

Read and act out the story as a play.

1. One person reads what Slim says.
2. One person reads what Luke says.
3. Two people play Slim and Luke.
4. Five people play the mules.

This Is a Nice Place

Use **is** and **are** to tell about now.

Beth **is** on a horse.
The trails **are** bumpy.

Use **was** and **were** to tell about the past.

Beth's horse **was** tired.
The other horses **were** at the ranch.

Talk

What if you rode a horse?
Where would you go?
Tell what the place is like.

Write

Write about a ranch or farm. Tell what's there.

Riddle-dee Fiddle-dee-dee

by Helen Lester
illustrated by Laura Ovresat

He, She, and Me
Up in a tree
Playing with riddles
Fiddle-dee-dee.

159

161

163

He, She, and Me

Up in a tree

Playing with riddles

Fiddle-dee-dee!

The Riddles

by Bernard Wiseman

Boris the Bear met Morris the Moose.

"Do you like riddles?" Boris asked.

Morris asked, "How do they taste?"

Boris said, "You do not eat riddles."

Morris asked, "Do you drink them?"

Boris said, "You do not eat riddles.
You do not drink riddles. You ask them!
Listen—I will ask you a riddle."

Boris asked, "What has four feet—"

Morris yelled, "ME!"

"I did not finish," Boris said.

"What has four feet and a tail—"

"ME!" Morris yelled.

"I still did not finish!" Boris cried.

"Let me finish!"

Morris put a hoof over his mouth.

Boris asked, "What has four feet and
a tail and flies?"

"ME!" Morris yelled. "I have four feet
and a tail, and flies come and sit on
me all the time!"

"No, no!" Boris growled.

"The answer is: A horse in an airplane!

"Here is another riddle. What kind of comb cannot comb hair?"

"I know!" Morris cried.

"A broken comb!"

"NO! NO! NO!" Boris shouted.

"The answer is a honeycomb!"

"What is a honeycomb?"
Morris asked.

Boris said, "It is the inside
of a bee house. Don't you
know anything?"

Morris said, "I know about riddles.
You do not eat riddles. You do not drink
riddles. You ASK riddles."

Boris said, "And you must answer them!

Try to answer this riddle.

What kind of bee does not sting?"

"I know!" cried Morris.

"A friendly bee!"

"NO! NO!" Boris yelled.

Morris cried, "A sleeping bee!"

"NO! NO! NO!" Boris shouted.

"The answer is: a beetle. Oh, you don't know how to answer the riddles. I am not going to ask you any more."

Morris said, "You know how to answer riddles. Let me ask you riddles."

"Go ahead," said Boris. "Ask me riddles."

Morris asked, "What has four feet and a tail and flies?"

Boris answered, "A horse in an airplane."

"No! No!" Morris cried. "A moose in
an airplane."

Boris yelled, "You mean a HORSE!"

Morris said, "I mean a moose. I want a
moose to get an airplane ride!"

Then Morris said, "Here is another riddle. What kind of beetle does not sting?"

Boris said, "You mean, what kind of BEE does not sting!"

Morris laughed. "I mean what kind of beetle! All bees sting!"

Boris shouted, "Oh, you don't
know anything about riddles!
I am going home!"

A bird asked Morris, "What is
he angry about?"

"Riddles," said Morris. "He
does not like them."

About the Author and Illustrator

Bernard Wiseman said, "I was a cartoonist long before I was a writer." He began drawing cartoons when he was a young sailor.

Mr. Wiseman wrote funny children's books. He said that they were like his cartoons. If you like funny books, you might enjoy reading other books about Morris and Boris.

Reader Response

Let's Talk

Would you rather ask riddles like Boris or answer riddles like Morris? Tell why.

Write a Riddle

Think of an animal.

Write clues about it.

Write *What am I?*

4 Ask a friend to answer your riddle.

Do Not Do That!

The word **not** changes what a sentence means.

This boy is writing riddles. This boy is **not** writing riddles.

Talk

What do you like to make?
Tell how to make it.
Are there things you should
not do when you make it?

Write

Write about how to
make something.

Glossary

Words from Your Stories

Aa

alone   **Alone** means without anyone else.

angry   When you are upset and mad about something, you are **angry**. Dad was **angry** when I broke the window.

angry

answer   To **answer** means to speak or write something when you are asked a question. Who will **answer** the question?

answer

Bb

before   Your turn comes **before** mine. Have you been to the zoo **before**?

Cc

catch   **Catch** means to take and hold something moving.

count   **Count** means to add up or find the number of something.

cousins   Your **cousins** are the children of any of your uncles or aunts.

cowboys   **Cowboys** are men who work on a cattle ranch or perform in rodeos.

Dd ─────────────────────────

different   **Different** means not alike. The dogs are all **different**.

different

Gg ─────────────────────────

growled   When an animal has **growled**, it has made a deep, angry sound.

Hh ─────────────────────────

heard   When the dog **heard** the sound, it began to bark.

hoof   A **hoof** is the hard part of the foot of some animals. Horses, cattle, sheep, and pigs have **hooves.**

hooray   **Hooray** is a shout of happiness.

hooray

Ii ─────────────────────────

idea   An **idea** is a thought or plan.

Ll

lightning **Lightning** is a flash of light in the sky.

lightning

lose When you **lose** something, you are not able to find it.

lullaby A **lullaby** is a soft song that quiets a baby so that it falls asleep.

Pp

pointed If you **pointed** to something, you showed it to someone using your finger.

proud **Proud** means thinking well of yourself or others.

pointed

Qq

quilt A **quilt** is a soft cover for a bed.

quilt

Rr

ranch A **ranch** is a very large farm and its buildings. Sheep, cattle, and horses are raised on **ranches.**

riddles   **Riddles** are puzzles that ask a question.

Ss

shining   When something is **shining**, it is giving off a bright light. The sun is **shining.**

shining

shouted   **Shouted** means called or yelled loudly.

stories   **Stories** tell about people and places and what happens to them.

Tt

thunder   **Thunder** is the loud noise that often follows lightning.

town   A **town** is a large group of houses and other buildings.

Ww

wears   When a person **wears** something, he or she has it on his or her body. The team **wears** matching baseball caps.

wears

wood   The trunk and branches of a tree are made of **wood.**

Tested Word List

The Red Stone Game
The Gingerbread Man

after
as
call
catch
laugh
something

The Same as You
Cherry Pies and Lullabies

every
made
mother
of
was

Rose and Grandma Make the Sun Shine
Our Family Get-Together

father
going
has
thank
very

The Rolling Rice Cake
The Rat and the Cat

be
friend
pretty
soon
your

June and the Mule: A Tall Tale
Slim, Luke, and the Mules

count
four
funny
long
watch
were

Riddle-dee Fiddle-dee-dee
The Riddles

about
answer
any
ask
kind
over

Acknowledgments

Text

Page 18: Adapted abridgment of *The Gingerbread Man* retold by Sally Bell, pp. 3–5, 7, 9–10, 13–14, 17–18, 21, 23–24, 26–28, & 31–32. Copyright © 1990 by Golden Books Publishing Company, Inc. All rights reserved. Reprinted by permission of Golden Books Publishing Company, Inc.
Page 50: *Cherry Pies and Lullabies* by Lynn Reiser, pp. 6–38. Copyright © 1998 by Lynn Whisnant Reiser. Reprinted by permission of Greenwillow Books, a division of William Morrow & Company, Inc.
Page 101: "Four Generations" from *Fathers, Mothers, Sisters, Brothers* by Mary Ann Hoberman, p. 5. Text copyright © 1991 by Mary Ann Hoberman. Reprinted by permission of Little, Brown and Company.
Page 112: Abridgment of "Sam's Story" from *Three by the Sea* by Edward Marshall, pictures by James Marshall, pp. 20–34. Text copyright © 1981 by Edward Marshall. Pictures copyright © 1981 by James Marshall. Reprinted by permission of Dial Books for Young Readers, a division of Penguin Putnam, Inc.
Page 128: "I Wouldn't" from *You Read to Me, I'll Read to You* by John Ciardi. Reprinted by permission of the Ciardi Family.
Page 166: "The Riddles" from *Morris and Boris, Three Stories* by Bernard Wiseman. Reprinted by permission of Susan N. Wiseman.

Artists

Maryjane Begin, cover, 8–9
Iskra Johnson, (calligraphy) 9
Elizabeth Allen, 10–17
Bob Barner, 18–40
Anastasia Mitchell, 41
Stacey Schuett, 42–49
Lynn Reiser, 50–73
Doris Ettlinger, 74–75
Darryl Ligasan, 76–83
Francisco X. Mora, 101
Marisol Sarrazin, 102–103
Oki Han, 104–111
Pamela Paulsrud, (calligraphy) 104
James Marshall, 112–127, 130a
Paige Miglio, 128–129
Anthony Lewis, 130b, 131
Kenneth J. Spengler, 132–139
Wendy Shaul, 140–153, 154b–e, 155
Reggie Holladay, 154a, 156–157
Laura Ovresat, 158–165
Janet Ocwieja, (props) 158
Bernard Wiseman, 166–185, 186a, 187b
Ellen Joy Sasaki, 186b, 187a

Photographs

Page 39 Courtesy Bob Barner
Page 73 Courtesy Lynn Reiser, Photo: Branka Whisnant
Pages 84–100 Jim Markham for Scott Foresman
Page 127 Courtesy Houghton Mifflin Co.
Page 155 Courtesy Wendy Shaul
Page 185 Courtesy Susan Wiseman

Glossary

The contents of this glossary have been adapted from *My First Picture Dictionary*, Revised Edition, Copyright © 1990 by Scott, Foresman and Company, or from *My Second Picture Dictionary*, Revised Edition, Copyright © 1990 by Scott, Foresman and Company.